grade
5

Eric Taylor

Music Theory in Practice

Revised edition 2008

The Associated Board of
the Royal Schools of Music

DO NOT
PHOTOCOPY
© MUSIC

Syllabus for ABRSM Grade 5

As in preceding grades, with the addition of:

(1) Irregular time signatures of $\frac{5}{4}$ $\frac{7}{4}$ $\frac{5}{8}$ $\frac{7}{8}$, and the grouping of notes and rests within these times. Irregular division of simple time values.

(2) Tenor clef (C clef centred on 4th line). The identification of notes in the four clefs in any of the keys set for this grade, and the transposition at the octave of a simple melody from any clef to another. The writing at concert pitch of a melody notated for an instrument in B$\flat$, A or F, and vice versa (the interval of transposition up or down will be given). The writing in open score, using treble and bass clefs, of a passage for SATB written on two staves, and vice versa.

(3) Scales and key signatures of all major and minor keys up to six sharps and flats. All simple and compound intervals from any note.

(4) The identification of $\frac{5}{3}$ and $\frac{6}{3}$ chords on the tonic, supertonic, subdominant and dominant in any of the keys set for this grade. The identification of the $\frac{6}{4}$ chord and of the progression $\frac{6}{4}$ $\frac{5}{3}$ on the dominant note in any of the keys set for this grade. The choice of suitable chords using any recognised method of notation at cadential points of a simple melody in the major keys of C, G, D or F.

(5) The composition of a simple melody of not more than eight bars, using a given opening and writing for a specific instrument (some choice will be given) or (at candidate's choice) the composition of a melody to given words. Appropriate performance directions relating to tempo, dynamics and articulation will be required.

(6) More terms and signs. The recognition of ornaments, including the replacement of written-out ornamentation with the appropriate signs, but not vice versa. Questions about a passage of music written for voices or instruments will include questions on the types of voice and names of instruments, the clefs they use, instrument family groups and the basic way by which they produce sound, as well as points of general musical observation designed to test the candidate's ability to apply theoretical knowledge to actual music.

First published 1990
Revised edition 2008
Reprinted in 2008

© 2008 by The Associated Board of the Royal Schools of Music (Publishing) Ltd

Typeset by Barnes Music Engraving Ltd
Cover by Økvik Design
Inside design by Vermillion
Printed in England by Headley Brothers Ltd, Ashford, Kent

Contents

Each chapter begins with a reference to *The AB Guide to Music Theory*, a book that supplies further background knowledge on each topic. Where keywords are introduced in the text, they are highlighted in **bold** and accompanied by a definition. In the quoted music examples, tempo marks without brackets occur in the original as shown. Tempo marks in brackets occur earlier in the music or are editorial.

Irregular time signatures

(The AB Guide to Music Theory, Chapters 1/2 and 5/3)

An **irregular** bar is a bar that you cannot divide into equal groups of two or three beats. The most common irregular bars have:

► five beats – **quintuple** time
► seven beats – **septuple** time

Here are some examples of irregular time signatures:

$\frac{5}{4}$ = five crotchets (quarter notes) in a bar $\frac{7}{4}$ = seven crotchets (quarter notes) in a bar

$\frac{5}{8}$ = five quavers (eighth notes) in a bar $\frac{7}{8}$ = seven quavers (eighth notes) in a bar

These are the only four irregular time signatures you will have to identify in Grade 5. It will not be too difficult to add bar-lines or time signatures in the exercises, so long as you count carefully!

Exercise 1  **Add bar-lines to these extracts. They all begin on the first beat of the bar.**

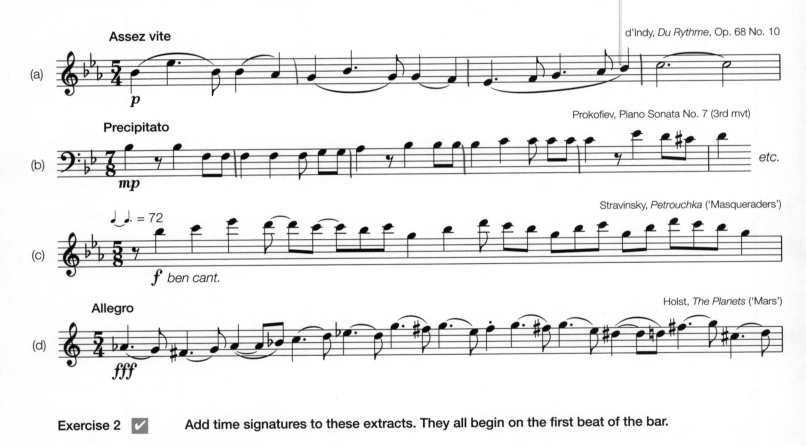

Exercise 2 ✔ **Add time signatures to these extracts. They all begin on the first beat of the bar.**

Allegretto

Mussorgsky, *The Nursery* (No. 1)

(c)

[*p*]

etc.

Gay (♪ = *c*.200)

Hindemith, *Ludus Tonalis* (Fuga 2)

(d)

mf

etc.

Exercise 3 ✔ These extracts all contain changes of time signature. Add time signatures where they are needed. They all begin on the first beat of the bar.

Shostakovich, String Quartet No. 2 (2nd mvt)

(a) **(Adagio)** ♩ = ♩ ♩ = ♩ ♩ = ♩ **poco accelerando**

f *p* *cresc.*

f

Moderato

Stravinsky, Octet for Wind Instruments (2nd mvt)

(b)

mf legatissimo

pp sub.

(♪ = *c*.96)

Copland, Duo for Flute and Piano (2nd mvt)

(c)

p

mp

Tenor clef

(The AB Guide to Music Theory, Chapter 4/7)

Both the alto and tenor clefs are C clefs (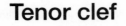): the only difference between them is their position on the stave. In the **alto clef** (which you studied in Grade 4) middle C is on the third line:

but in the **tenor clef** middle C is on the fourth line:

This is how key signatures of up to five sharps or flats are arranged:

The tenor clef may be used by cellos, bassoons and tenor trombones.

Exercise 1 ✔ **Write the name of each of these notes. (The first answer is given as an example.)**

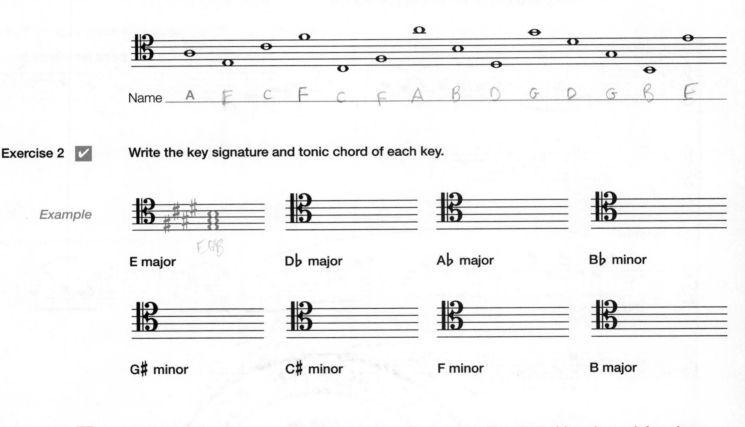

Name A E C F C F A B D G D G B E

Exercise 2 ✔ **Write the key signature and tonic chord of each key.**

Example

E major   Db major   Ab major   Bb minor

G# minor   C# minor   F minor   B major

Exercise 3 ✔ **Rewrite each of these passages at the same pitch, using either the treble or bass clef as shown. Remember to include the key signature, time signature and any performance directions.**

Example

Presto

Glinka, *Ruslan and Ludmila* (Overture)

mf cantabile

Presto

mf cantabile

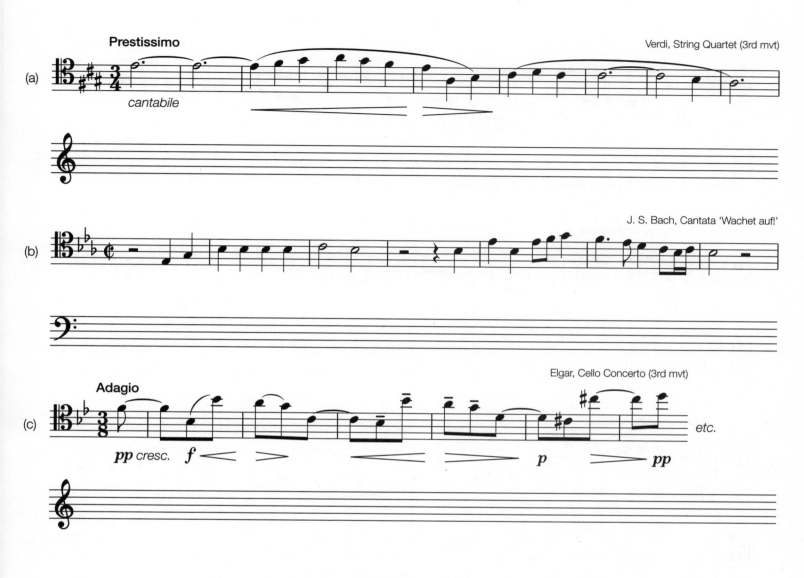

Exercise 4 ☑ Rewrite these extracts at the same pitch in the tenor clef. Remember to include the key signature.

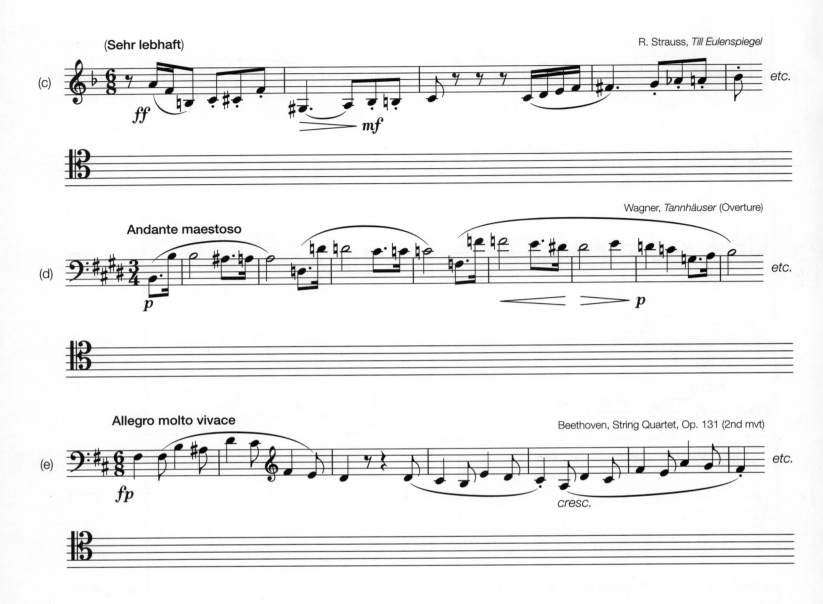

Major and minor keys up to six sharps and flats

(The AB Guide to Music Theory, Chapter 4/1–3)

You studied keys with up to five sharps or flats in Grade 4. In Grade 5, you will study keys with six sharps or flats. They are:

► F♯ major – six sharps
► D♯ minor – six sharps

► G♭ major – six flats
► E♭ minor – six flats

F♯ major and G♭ major are **enharmonic** equivalents – their scales sound the same but they are written differently. Look at the examples on the next page.

Remember! When two notes have the same sound but different names, they are called enharmonics. For example, C♯ is the enharmonic of D♭, and vice versa.

Enharmonic examples

F# major

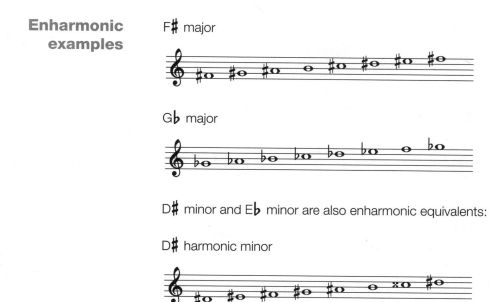

Gb major

D# minor and Eb minor are also enharmonic equivalents:

D# harmonic minor

(the descending form uses the same notes)

Eb harmonic minor

(the descending form uses the same notes)

D# melodic minor

Eb melodic minor

Composers sometimes write pieces in more complicated keys: e.g. seven sharps (C# major / A# minor) or seven flats (Cb major / Ab minor). But composers usually avoid these keys and use simpler enharmonic equivalents instead. C# major, for example, is more easily written as Db major (five flats instead of seven sharps). D# minor, too, is rare: composers usually write in Eb minor instead.

Key signatures with six sharps or flats are arranged like this – notice the patterns for each clef:

Exercise 1 ✔ Add accidentals where necessary to make these scales. (Do not use key signatures.)

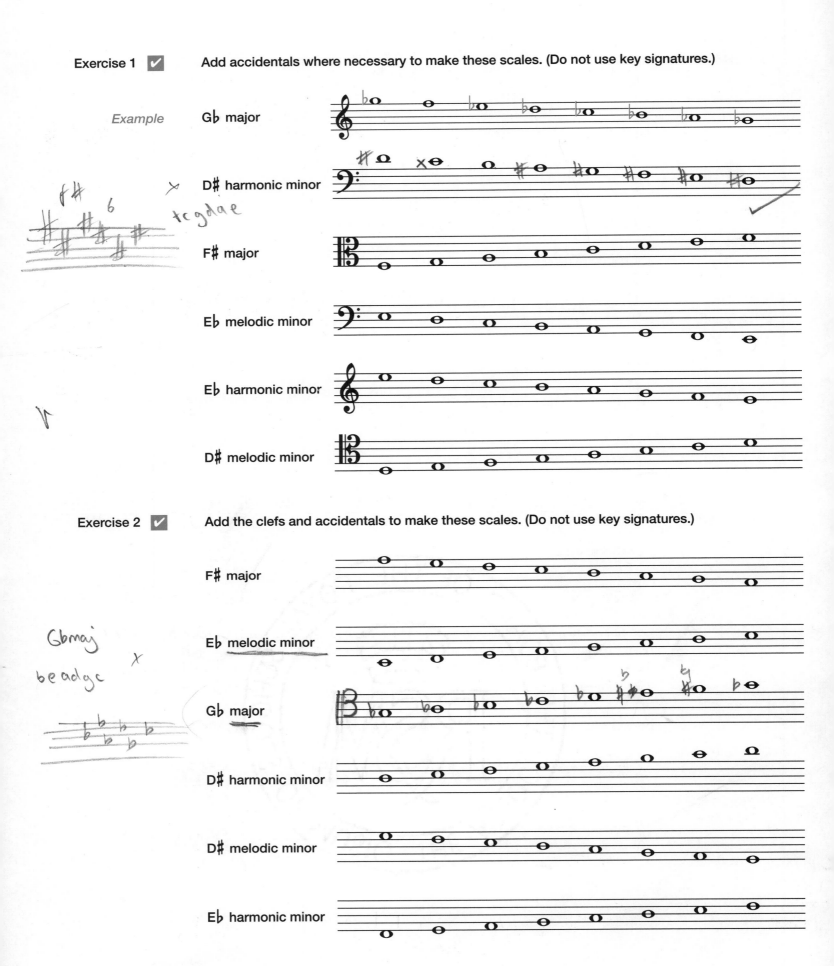

Example   G♭ major

D♯ harmonic minor

F♯ major

E♭ melodic minor

E♭ harmonic minor

D♯ melodic minor

Exercise 2 ✔ Add the clefs and accidentals to make these scales. (Do not use key signatures.)

F♯ major

E♭ melodic minor

G♭ major

D♯ harmonic minor

D♯ melodic minor

E♭ harmonic minor

Exercise 3 ☑   Write the key signature followed by the tonic triad, after each clef in these keys.

F♯ major

D♯ minor

G♭ major

E♭ minor

Exercise 4 ☑   Name the key of each extract. Then rewrite each extract using the correct key signature. Remove any accidentals that become unnecessary, but remember also to add any that may be needed.

Example

Dvořák, *Humoreske*, Op. 101 No. 7

Key   G♭ major

J. S. Bach, 48 Preludes & Fugues, Bk II (Fugue No. 8)

(a)

Key   D♯min

(b) Tchaikovsky, Overture '1812'

Key _____

(c) Rachmaninoff, *Élégie*, Op. 3 No. 1

Key _____

(d) Puccini, *Madam Butterfly* ('One fine day')

Key _____

Exercise 5 ☑   (i) Rewrite these extracts enharmonically. Use key signatures of six sharps, but do not change how it will sound.

(ii) Rewrite these extracts enharmonically. Use key signatures of six flats, but do not change how it will sound. (Notice the change of clef in the second example.)

Transposition

(The AB Guide to Music Theory, Chapter 7/2)

In the exam, you will have to transpose a melody. You may need to use any of these intervals:

(1) up or down an **octave**;
(2) up or down a **major 2nd**;
(3) up or down a **minor 3rd**;
(4) up or down a **perfect 5th**.

These four intervals are used by the transposing instruments in the orchestra. You can read more about them in *The AB Guide to Music Theory, Part II, Chapters 19 & 20.*

> **Remember!** When you transpose a melody by a major, minor or perfect interval, the tonality will remain the same. For example, the key of C major transposed down a minor 3rd will be A major, not A minor.

Transposition up or down an octave

You studied transposition at the octave in Grade 3, using the treble and bass clefs. In Grade 5, you will also need to use the alto and tenor clefs. When you are familiar with these clefs it should not be too difficult – but make sure that you do actually *transpose* the passage (rather than merely rewrite it at the same pitch in a different clef), and also that you transpose it one octave and not two.

Exercise 1 ✔   **Write this passage an octave lower in each clef.**

Poco adagio; cantabile

Haydn, String Quartet, Op. 76 No. 3 (2nd mvt)

p dolce

etc.

Exercise 2 Write this passage an octave higher in each clef.

Exercise 3 Write this passage an octave higher in the treble clef, and an octave lower in the bass clef.

Exercise 4 ☑   **Write this passage an octave higher in the treble clef, and an octave lower in the bass clef.**

J. S. Bach, B minor Mass (Kyrie)

Transposition up or down a major second

When instruments 'in B flat' (such as clarinets in B♭, trumpets in B♭) play middle C, the note you will hear is the B♭ below. In other words, instruments in B♭ produce sounds that are a major 2nd lower than the written notes. For example, a melody written like this:

actually sounds like this:

The pitch at which the music is actually heard is called **concert pitch** or **sounding pitch**.

For an instrument in B♭ to produce these sounds:

the notes have to be written a major 2nd higher – this is called **written pitch**

As you can see in the examples above, the key signatures as well as the notes are transposed.

> Remember!   **Concert pitch describes the naming of notes as they actually sound, as opposed to how they appear on the page. For example, on a B♭ instrument such as trumpet or clarinet, 'written C' is the same as 'concert B♭'.**

Accidentals

You also need to be careful with the accidentals that occur in a melody. Note that:

▶ An accidental may have to be changed in the transposed version: e.g. on page 16, the F natural in the first example becomes E *flat* in the transposed version.

▶ A chromatically altered note must be replaced by its exact equivalent and not by an enharmonic substitute. (It is true that, for various special reasons, composers do occasionally use enharmonic substitutes, but these are exceptions.) The F natural in the first example (flattened 7th in G major) becomes E flat in the transposed version (flattened 7th in F major) – not D sharp.

Until the early 20th century, horn and trumpet parts were written without a key signature, whatever the key: accidentals were added before individual notes as necessary. However, in the following exercises, and in the Grade 5 exam, you should assume that a key signature is to be used unless there is an instruction to the contrary (as in Exercise 11, page 22).

Except where a transposed part is written without a key signature (as in Exercise 11, page 22), *every* accidental in the original requires a corresponding accidental in the transposed version. Do not try to 'improve' on the given music by leaving out an accidental where one in the original was not strictly necessary. (The composer might have put it there as a sensible precaution, e.g. something being played by another instrument might cause confusion.)

Practise your transposing skills in the following exercises. Remember to make the necessary changes to key signatures.

Exercise 5 ✔

These passages are notated for instruments in B♭. Write them out at concert pitch, i.e. a major 2nd lower. (The beginning of (a) has been done as an example.)

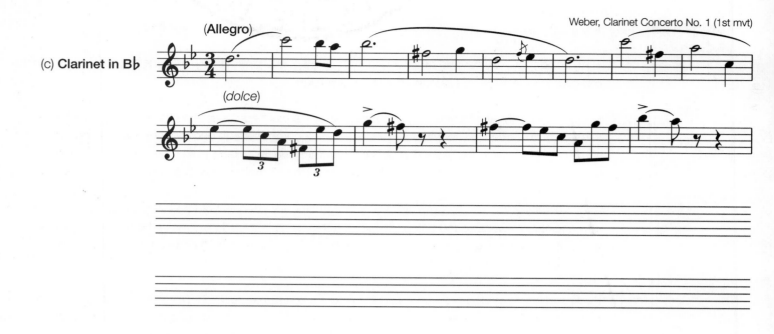

(c) Clarinet in B♭

Weber, Clarinet Concerto No. 1 (1st mvt)

Exercise 6 ☑ Transpose these passages up a major 2nd, so that they will sound at concert pitch when played by instruments in B♭. (The beginning of (a) has been done as an example.)

(a) Allegro amabile — Brahms, Clarinet Sonata No. 2 (1st mvt)

Clarinet in B♭ — Allegro amabile

(b) Larghetto — Mozart, Divertimento, K.Anh.229 No. 2

Clarinet in B♭

(c) (Presto ♩ = 152) — Elgar, *2nd Wand of Youth Suite* ('The Wild Bears')

Trumpet in B♭

Transposition up and down a minor 3rd

The concert pitch of instruments 'in A' is a minor 3rd lower than it is written. For example, if you play a written middle C on either a clarinet in A or on a trumpet in A, the note that you actually hear is the A below. So music that is written in C major actually sounds like A major. In the same way, you would have to write music in E♭ major if you want it to have a concert pitch of C major.

Exercise 7 ✔ These passages are notated for instruments in A. Write them out at concert pitch, i.e. a minor 3rd lower. (The beginning of (a) has been done as an example.)

Exercise 8 ✔ Transpose these passages up a minor 3rd, so that they will sound at concert pitch when played by instruments in A. (The beginning of (a) has been done as an example.)

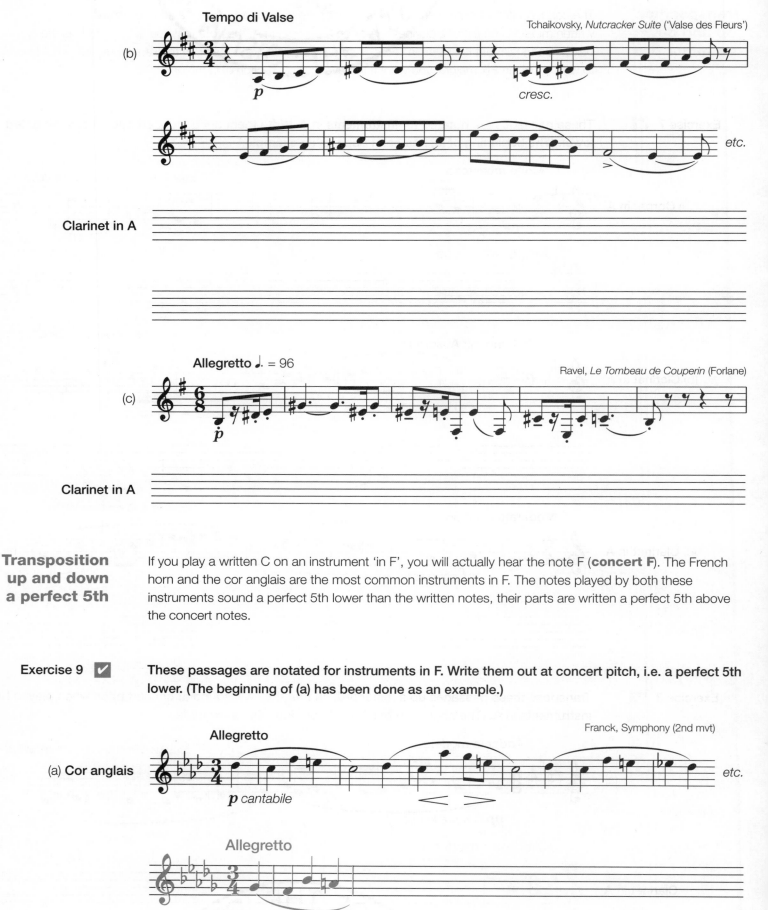

Tempo di Valse

Tchaikovsky, *Nutcracker Suite* ('Valse des Fleurs')

(b)

p

cresc.

etc.

Clarinet in A

Allegretto ♩. = 96

Ravel, *Le Tombeau de Couperin* (Forlane)

(c)

p

Clarinet in A

Transposition up and down a perfect 5th

If you play a written C on an instrument 'in F', you will actually hear the note F (**concert F**). The French horn and the cor anglais are the most common instruments in F. The notes played by both these instruments sound a perfect 5th lower than the written notes, their parts are written a perfect 5th above the concert notes.

Exercise 9 ☑ **These passages are notated for instruments in F. Write them out at concert pitch, i.e. a perfect 5th lower. (The beginning of (a) has been done as an example.)**

Franck, Symphony (2nd mvt)

(a) Cor anglais

Allegretto

p cantabile

etc.

Allegretto

p cantabile

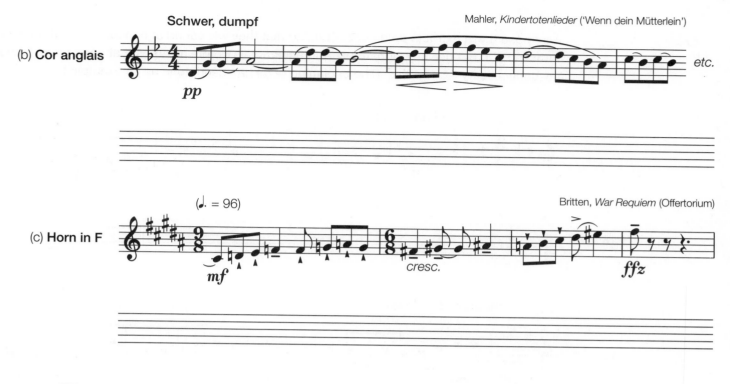

Exercise 10 ✔ Transpose these extracts up a perfect 5th, so that they will sound at concert pitch when played by instruments in F. Decide whether it is best to use treble or bass clefs. (The beginning of (a) has been done as an example.)

Exercise 11 ✔ Transpose these extracts up a perfect 5th, so that they will sound at concert pitch when played by horns in F. Do not use key signatures. Add accidentals before all notes that need them: take away any unnecessary accidentals. (The beginning of (a) has been done as an example.)

(The AB Guide to Music Theory, Part II, Chapter 14/2)

Most choral music uses a combination of four different voices: soprano, alto, tenor and bass. The music for these four separate parts is written on either two or four staves.

▶ In a two-stave layout, the upper voices – soprano and alto – are written in the treble clef on the top stave; and the two lower voices – tenor and bass – are written in the bass clef on the bottom stave.

▶ In a four-stave layout, each part has its own stave in the order of soprano, alto, tenor, bass.

▶ When different voices share a stave, it is called **short score**.

▶ When each voice has a stave of its own, it is called **open score**.

Remember!	**SATB is short for:**
	Soprano
	Alto
	Tenor
	Bass

The staves are given separate bar-lines, both in short and open score, like this:

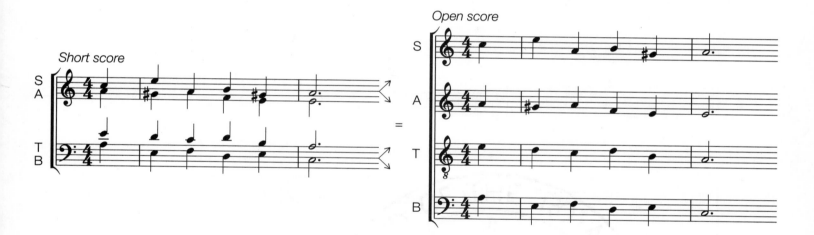

Short score

Open score

You may be asked to transcribe into open score a passage written in short score, or the other way round. The examples above show three important points:

(1) In short score the tenor part is written in the bass clef (at its true pitch); but in open score it is written in the treble clef, an *octave higher* than it actually sounds. (It is advisable to write a small 8 under the tenor's treble clef to show that the music sounds an octave lower than written.)

(2) In short score the stems of soprano and tenor notes always go up, wherever they are on the stave; and the stems of alto and bass notes always go down. Whenever two parts on the same stave share the same pitch you must draw a stem for each voice. However, if the note value is a semibreve (whole note) you must write two overlapping semibreves (whole note) on the stave, like this **oo** to represent both voices.

(3) When two vocal lines share the same stave, an accidental before a note in one part must be written again if the same note occurs in the other part later in the same bar. Look at the second ♯ (to the G) in the short-score example: it is necessary here, although it would not be needed in piano music.

Exercise 1 ✔   Transcribe these extracts into short score – the words are not shown. (The beginning of (a) has been done as an example.)

Purcell, Anthem 'Rejoice in the Lord alway'

J. S. Bach, Chorale 'Wer weiss, wie nahe mir' (Cantata 166)

Exercise 2 Transcribe these extracts into open score. (The beginning of (a) has been done as an example.)

(Allegretto con spirito)

Sullivan, *The Mikado* (Madrigal)

(a)

(Allegretto con spirito)

Beethoven, Symphony No. 9 (4th mvt)

(Allegro assai)

(b)

More irregular time divisions

(The AB Guide to Music Theory, Chapter 5/5a)

You have already studied the most common irregular time divisions: triplets (in Grade 2) and duplets (in Grade 4). The next two exercises use some more elaborate groups. In all of them, the irregular group replaces a 'simple time' unit (i.e. one that would normally divide into 2, 4, 8 etc.)

▶ A group of 5, 6 or 7 uses the same time values as a group of 4.
▶ A group of 9 uses the same values as a group of 8.

Exercise 1 ☑   Complete these sentences by adding ♪ or ♩ or 𝅗𝅥

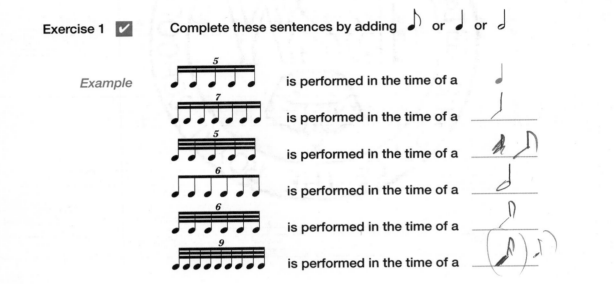

Example   is performed in the time of a

is performed in the time of a _____

is performed in the time of a _____

is performed in the time of a _____

is performed in the time of a _____

is performed in the time of a _____

Exercise 2 ☑   Add bar-lines to these extracts. They all begin on the first beat of the bar.

Heller, Prelude, Op. 119 No. 30

Vaughan Williams, Symphony No. 4 (1st mvt)

Liszt, *Hungarian Folksong* No. 4

Tchaikovsky, *Nutcracker Suite* ('Danse Arabe')

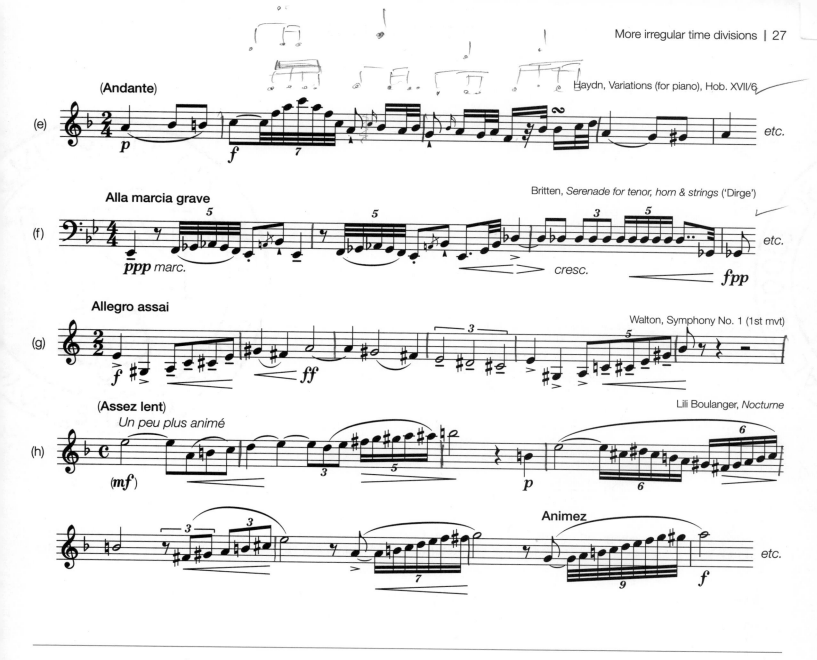

Intervals

(The AB Guide to Music Theory, Chapter 7/1 & 3)

In Grade 5, you must be able to describe the interval between any two notes. Sometimes the two notes may be more than one octave apart.

You can describe intervals of less than an octave in the same way that you did at Grade 4. For example, this is a diminished 5th:

whatever the key signature (if there is one):

Intervals of more than one octave are called **compound intervals**. You can describe compound intervals in two ways, like this:

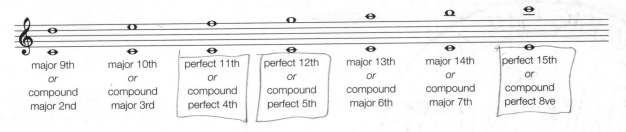

| major 9th *or* compound major 2nd | major 10th *or* compound major 3rd | perfect 11th *or* compound perfect 4th | perfect 12th *or* compound perfect 5th | major 13th *or* compound major 6th | major 14th *or* compound major 7th | perfect 15th *or* compound perfect 8ve |

Musicians generally refer to a '9th', '10th', '12th' and '15th' rather than to a 'compound 2nd' or a 'compound 3rd' etc. However, in the exam both forms of description are acceptable.

Exercise 1 ☑ **Write in the note that is needed to make each of these harmonic intervals.**

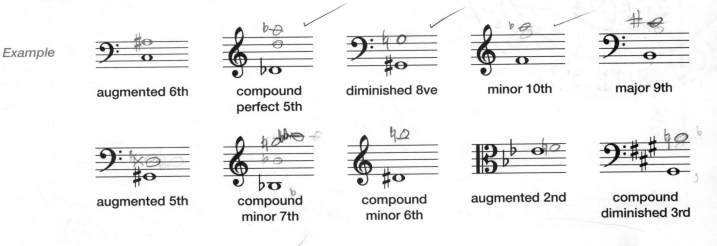

Example

augmented 6th — compound perfect 5th — diminished 8ve — minor 10th — major 9th

augmented 5th — compound minor 7th — compound minor 6th — augmented 2nd — compound diminished 3rd

Exercise 2 ☑ **Describe each of these harmonic intervals, e.g. augmented 4th, minor 10th (or compound minor 3rd) etc. Look at the key signature carefully, in case it affects either of the notes in the interval.**

Example

Augmented 5th — augmented 12th / compound aug 5th — major 7th — major 11th / compound maj 4th — minor 7th

Augmented 9th — diminished 14th — Augmented 6th — Augmented 11th — minor 9th

augmented 7th — diminished 12th — minor 6th — diminished 5th —

Exercise 3 ✔ 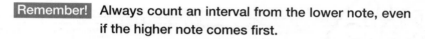 Describe each of the melodic intervals marked ⌐1⌐ ⌐2⌐ etc. in these extracts. Look carefully at the key signature and any accidentals in the bar. (The answers to numbers 1 and 2 in (a) have been done as an example.)

> **Remember!** Always count an interval from the lower note, even if the higher note comes first.

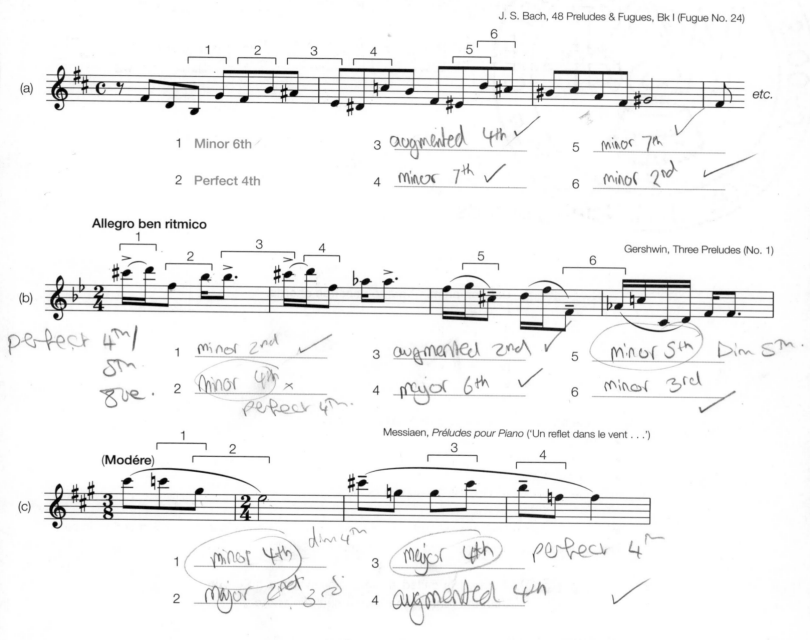

J. S. Bach, 48 Preludes & Fugues, Bk I (Fugue No. 24)

(a)
1 Minor 6th
2 Perfect 4th
3 augmented 4th ✔
4 minor 7th ✔
5 minor 7th
6 minor 2nd ✔

Allegro ben ritmico

Gershwin, Three Preludes (No. 1)

(b)

perfect 4th / 5th / 8ve.

1 minor 2nd ✔
2 minor 4th × perfect 4th
3 augmented 2nd ✔
4 major 6th ✔
5 minor 5th Dim 5th
6 minor 3rd ✔

Messiaen, *Préludes pour Piano* ('Un reflet dans le vent . . .')

(Modére)

(c)
1 minor 4th dim 4th
2 major 2nd 3rd
3 major 4th perfect 4th
4 augmented 4th ✔

Mozart, *Così fan tutte* (Act II, 'Per pietà')

(Adagio)

(d)
min.
1 Maj 7th
2 Maj 13th minor
3 maj 2nd
4 maj 10th
5 maj 12th
6 min 3rd

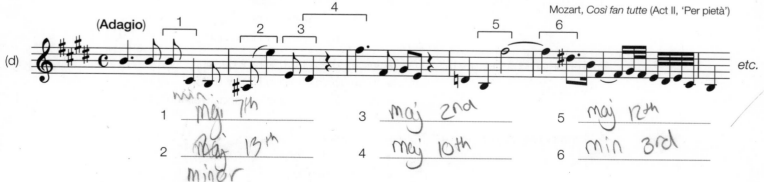

Exercise 4   This extract for alto and bass soloists, is taken from Purcell's *Te Deum* in D. Name the harmonic intervals between the bass and alto voices at the points indicated by dotted lines. (The first answer is given as an example.)

etc.

1 Perfect 5th   3 _____   5 _____

2 _____   4 _____   6 _____

Naming chords

(The AB Guide to Music Theory, Chapter 8/2)

Remember! **Use roman numbers to describe chords:**

I   =   1
II   =   2
III   =   3
IV   =   4
V   =   5

In Grade 4 you identified these chords in root position:
▶ tonic (I),
▶ subdominant (IV),
▶ dominant (V).
In Grade 5 you will also look at the supertonic (II).

In the exam, you will need to say which note is the lowest note of the chord (root, 3rd or 5th), in other words, which **inversion** the chord is in. You can do this in different ways.

Remember! **A chord is called an inversion when a note other than the tonic is the lowest sounding note.**

(1) One way is to add 'a', 'b' or 'c':
  ▶ 'a' – means root position,
  ▶ 'b' – means first inversion,
  ▶ 'c' – means second inversion,

to the roman number, like this:
  ▶ Ia = tonic chord in root position,
  ▶ Ib = tonic chord in first inversion,
  ▶ Ic = tonic chord in second inversion.

(2) Another way is to write:
  ▶ $\frac{5}{3}$ instead of 'a',
  ▶ $\frac{6}{3}$ instead of 'b',
  ▶ $\frac{6}{4}$ instead of 'c',

after the roman number.

These numbers refer to intervals from the bass note, for example:

IV $\frac{6}{3}$ = the first inversion of the subdominant chord.

(3) Many people use the roman number on its own to describe a root-position chord, for example, just II (without either 'a' or '$\frac{5}{3}$'). The roman number on its own, therefore, means a root-position chord.

You can use any of the chord symbols, just make sure that the symbol is clear and fully describes the function of the chord in the key.

Exercise 1 ✔   **Name the keys of the following extracts. Identify the chords marked with * and indicate which of the notes is the lowest note of the chord (or which position the chord is in).**

Example

Key Bb major   IIb   V   I

Presto   Mendelssohn, Song without Words, Op. 102 No. 3

(a)

Key C maj

Andante   Mozart, *The Magic Flute* (Act II, March)

(b)

Key F maj

J. S. Bach, Chorale 'Wer nur den lieben Gott lässen' (Cantata 88)

(c)   *etc.*

Key _____

Beethoven, Piano Sonata, Op. 10 No. 3 (Menuetto)

Key _____

Handel, Air, from HWV 434

Key _____

Purcell, *Dido and Aeneas* ('When monarchs unite')

Key _____

Shostakovich, 24 Preludes & Fugues, No. 19 (Prelude)

Key _____

Composing a melody

At Grade 5 you will need to compose a short melody of no more than eight bars.

Instrument or voice?

You can decide whether to compose for an instrument, e.g. violin, cello, clarinet or trumpet, or for voice. You do not need to know a lot about the instrument that you choose, but you should think about its style and characteristics. For example, you need to know the lowest note that the instrument can play, and if you are composing for a violin, for example, you could include some pizzicato if it is suitable for the melody. (*The AB Guide to Music Theory*, Part II, Chapters 19–20 has more information about instruments.)

In the Grade 5 exam you will have these options:

► If you choose to compose for an instrument, you will be given the start of the melody.

► If you choose to compose for voice, you will be given words but not an opening.

If you decide to compose for voice, remember that the pitch range is usually much smaller than for an instrument. Try to keep within a range of a 12th.

General advice

► You do not need to write more than eight bars – this includes the opening for an instrumental melody. It is a good idea to write exactly eight bars since eight-bar melodies are very common and are the easiest to compose. Much instrumental music and many well-known songs, new and old, are made up of eight-bar melodies.

► Your melody should be finished – do not leave it open-ended so that the melody sounds as if it needs something else to finish it off.

Performance directions

Include some performance directions (you will not need many in an eight-bar melody).

Here are some suggestions:

► Decide how fast you want the melody to be performed and add a tempo direction, e.g. **Allegro**, **Andante** or a metronome mark.

► Show the dynamic level that you want, e.g. **$\textit{mf}$**, **$\textit{p}$**. If you want to change the speed or dynamic level, give the necessary directions, e.g. **rit.**, ———————

► Add phrasing (articulation) marks, e.g. legato slurs and staccato dots. Be careful when you draw slurs. Be clear at which note they start and finish. If there is only one voice or instrument on the stave, you normally place the slur on the same side as the note-heads when these all go in the same direction. If the stems go up and down, the slur usually goes above the notes. Put ties and staccato marks inside or below the slur, not above it.

Listen to your melody

Writing a melody is a challenge to your inventiveness and imagination. You should always try to hear in your mind what you have written. During the exam you will not be able to try your melody on an instrument or sing it out loud. However, it is very helpful to do this when practising, particularly in the early stages; and it is always a good idea to play a melody when you have finished it, to see whether you have actually written the sounds you intended.

Rhythm and pitch

The most important features in a melody are (i) its rhythmic organisation and (ii) the melodic shapes produced by the pitch of each note. Look at the rhythm and pitch shapes in the examples that follow. In most of these extracts you will see a 'V' printed below the stave, half-way through the melody. This indicates a cadence point, which you will read more about on page 38.

Este's Psalter, 1592

(a) While shep - herds watched their flocks by night, All seat - ed on the ground, The an - gel of the Lord came down, And glo - ry shone a - round.

Stravinsky, *Petrouchka* ('The Shrove-Tide Fair')

(b)

Traditional, 'Barb'ra Allen'

(c) In Scar - let town, where I was born, There was a fair maid dwellin', Made ev - 'ry youth cry 'well - a - way!' Her name was Bar - b'ra Al - len.

J. Clarke, *The Prince of Denmark's March*

(d)

Andante

Haydn, Trumpet Concerto (2nd mvt)

(e)

Handel, *Scipione* (March)

Traditional

Sing a song of six - pence, A poc - ket - ful of rye, Four - and - twen - ty

black - birds baked in a pie, When the pie was o - pened the birds be - gan to

sing: O was - n't that a dain - ty dish to set be - fore a king!

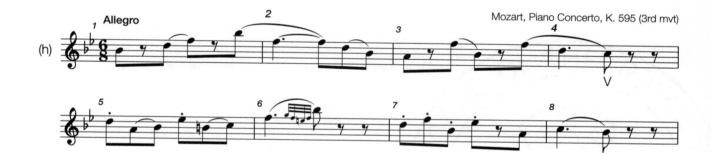

Allegro

Mozart, Piano Concerto, K. 595 (3rd mvt)

Purcell

Nymphs and shep - herds come a - way, come a - way; Nymphs and shep - herds

etc.

come a - way, come a - way, come, come, come, come a - way.

Rhythm

When you plan the rhythm of a melody, look at what was said about four-bar rhythms in Grade 2 (pages 23–25) and Grade 3 (pages 32–34) of *Music Theory in Practice*. Those suggestions apply equally to the rhythms of eight-bar melodies. Look at the following features in the melodies on pages 34 and 35 of this book. (The letters in brackets below refer to the examples, but now only their rhythms are shown.)

(1) The rhythm of bars 1–4 is repeated exactly in bars 5–8:

(2) The two halves are very nearly but not exactly the same:

(3) The two halves start the same but finish differently:

(4) The two halves start differently but finish the same, or very nearly so:

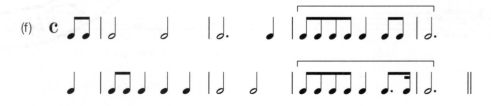

(5) The opening rthythm is used again in the second quarter of the tune:

(g) 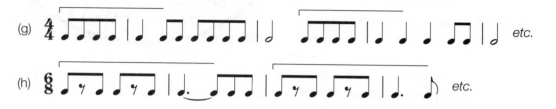 etc.

(h) 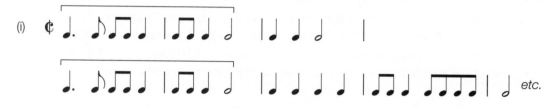 etc.

(6) The melody does not divide into equal sections: 'Nymphs and shepherds' consists of 3 + 5 bars, with the opening rhythm occurring again in bar 4:

(i)

 etc.

Pitch

When an opening rhythm occurs again later in a melody, the same notes may be played again, so the repetition of the music is exact, as in Examples (d) and (i). However, an absolutely exact repetition can sound boring. To avoid this, the pattern of the notes may be modified, e.g. in Example (b) where the notes are all moved down one degree:

Each half of tune (b) contains another rhythmic repetition:

Here, the notes in the second half (bars 6–8) are not the same as those in the first half (bars 2–4); however, the three descending quavers at the start of bar 3 are matched by three descending quavers at the start of bar 7:

Exact or modified repetitions of the opening music occur most frequently at the start of the second half of the melody, as in Example (d). They are also common at the beginning of the second quarter, as in Example (g):

Shape

The *overall* shape produced by the notes is very important.

(1) A melody should have a sense of direction. In (a) 'While shepherds watched', for example, the melody gradually moves upwards until it reaches the D in bar 5, and then gradually comes down again. The first half of the melody goes up, and the second half goes down: upward movement is balanced by downward movement. But neither half goes *straight* up or straight down. Both halves contain smaller ascents and descents. This is only one possible shape, however: the high point does not have to be half-way through a melody. There are many ways in which ascending and descending movement may be balanced and contrasted. But try to avoid circling around the same few notes!

(2) The second point concerns **cadences**, and the chords that they imply. Apart from some folksongs and other special cases, most melodies are inseparably connected with their supporting harmonies, particularly at the cadence points. Thus, the final note of a melody will belong to the tonic chord (the chord that most compositions almost always end with), and will usually be the tonic note itself. The chord most commonly found at a cadence during the course of a melody (generally half-way through) will be the dominant. Notice that, in most of the melodies (a) to (i) on pages 34–35, the note at the half-way point belongs to the dominant chord – though it is not necessarily the dominant note itself. (These points have been shown by a 'V' printed below the melody.)

Setting a melody to words

A melody set to words needs to be shaped in the same way as a purely instrumental melody. The words themselves may suggest musical ideas – mood, rhythmic patterns, pitch shape, and so on. The difficulty is that the melody must fit the words, and it will be partly judged by its suitability as a setting of them (see *Music Theory in Practice*, Grade 4, pages 29–33). For example, the character of the melody must reflect the mood of the words: a bright and cheerful melody would clearly be unsuitable for sad words. Similarly, the shape of the melody should help to highlight the important words.

Look at the two settings below of a verse by Allan Cunningham. Its rhythmic aspect was discussed in *Music Theory in Practice*, Grade 4 (pages 29–31). The following settings both use 'Version 4' from that book: i.e. their rhythms are identical. The first setting (below) adds emphasis to certain words (cold, snow, sleep, prim[roses]), by placing them at the top of each melodic curve, with 'sleep' as the highest note of all. The second setting is poor because the music does not match the words: the shape of the melody does nothing to bring out the meaning of the words; and its high point (the top G) is not suitable for a weak syllable.

Setting 1 (good ✔)

Setting 2 (poor ✗)

In both of these settings each syllable has only one note. However, syllables may of course be set to two or more notes, as in Setting 3 on the next page.

Setting 3 (good ✔)

Gone were but the win-ter cold,_____ And gone were but the snow,_____ I could

sleep_____ in the wild__ woods__ Where prim - ro - ses blow.

Setting particular syllables to two or more notes can help to bring out the meaning of the words – but be warned: it can also do precisely the opposite! For the best results, it is important to try and hear what you write.

Remember! Only the clef and the key signature should be shown at the beginning of the second and later staves – *not* the time signature. The only exception is when there is a change of time signature at the start of a new stave – and then the new time signature should also be shown after the bar-line at the end of the previous stave.

Exercise 1 ✔

Compose a melody up to eight bars in length, using the following openings. Write for one of the suggested instruments (write out your choice on the line before the first blank stave). You may substitute a different clef for the one given, provided it is appropriate to the selected instrument. Remember to include performance directions (tempo, phrasing, dynamics etc.)

Example — for violin, oboe or trumpet

Oboe — Allegretto — *mf* — *p*

(a) — for violin, flute or oboe

oboe

(f) for violin, oboe or clarinet

(g) for oboe, horn or trumpet

(h) for viola, clarinet or bassoon

(i) for violin, flute or oboe

Exercise 2 ☑ Compose a melody of up to eight bars in length to go with the following words. Put each syllable clearly under the note or notes to which it belongs. Indicate the appropriate speed and other necessary performance directions.

(a) But slumber hold me tightly till I waken in the dawn,
And hear the thrushes singing in the lilacs round the lawn. *Robert Louis Stevenson*

(b) For I dipt into the future, far as human eye could see,
Saw the Vision of the world, and all the wonder that would be. *Alfred Tennyson*

(c) I shall remember while the light lives yet,
And in the night time I shall not forget. *Algernon Swinburne*

(d)   The day begins to droop,
        Its course is done:
    But nothing tells the place
        Of the setting sun.   *Robert Bridges*

(e)   Who has seen the wind?
        Neither you nor I:
    But when the trees bow down their heads
        The wind is passing by.   *Christina Rossetti*

(f)   The Camel's hump is an ugly lump
    Which well you may see at the Zoo;
    But uglier yet is the Hump we get
    From having too little to do.   *Rudyard Kipling*

(g)   A flea met a fly in a flue,
             Said the flea let us fly,
             Said the fly let us flee,
             So they flew through a flaw in the flue.   *Nursery Rhyme*

(h)   Young Ben he was a nice young man,
             A carpenter by trade;
             And he fell in love with Sally Brown,
             That was a lady's maid.   *Thomas Hood*

(i)   April, April,
             Laugh thy golden laughter;
             Then, the moment after
             Weep thy golden tears!   *William Watson*

(j)   Only a man harrowing clods
          In a slow, silent walk,
      With an old horse that stumbles and nods
          Half asleep as they stalk.   *Thomas Hardy*

(k)   Wee folk, good folk,
          Trooping all together;
      Green jacket, red cap,
          And white owl's feather!   *William Allingham*

(l)   This is
      Where the river
      Runs down to the sea,
      Listen to its music, hear this mystery!   *Sacheverell Sitwell*

(The AB Guide to Music Theory, Chapter 12/1–2)

In Grade 5 you must be able to replace written-out ornaments with ornament signs.

For example, becomes

Do not be confused by the fact that there may be other possible interpretations of the appropriate ornament apart from the one given: e.g. the above turn might also be played like this:

(Remember to add any necessary accidentals.)

Exercise 1 ☑ **Rewrite the following passages using ornament signs to replace the notes in brackets.**

Chords at cadential points

(The AB Guide to Music Theory, Chapter 9/2)

In the exam, you will be asked to choose chords for a simple melody in C, G, D or F major. You will only need to know the chords on the tonic, supertonic, subdominant and dominant (I, II, IV and V for each of these keys). They will be used at points in the melody where there is a **cadence**.

These are the chords most commonly used at cadences.

    ▶ V – I   =   **perfect cadence**
    ▶ IV – I   =   **plagal cadence**
    ▶ (any chord) – V   =   **imperfect cadence**.

In Grade 5, therefore, an imperfect cadence may be either I–V, or II–V or IV–V.

You may also be asked to use or identify a $^6_4$ $^5_3$ chord progression. This is a good sequence to use when preparing a perfect or imperfect cadence point on the dominant note (where $^6_4$ refers to chord Ic and $^5_3$ refers to chord V).

There are a number of different ways to indicate a chord. You can:
(1) use roman numerals ('I', 'V' etc.)
(2) show how it might appear in jazz and popular music (e.g. 'Dm'),
(3) add a figured bass (e.g. $^5_3$)
(4) write out the notes in full on the staves.

You can choose to write chords it in any of these ways, just make sure it is clear!

Harmonizing notes

Most degrees of the major scale can be harmonized in two ways, using the chords listed above. But there are no alternative chords for the 3rd and the 7th degrees. These are the possibilities in C major:

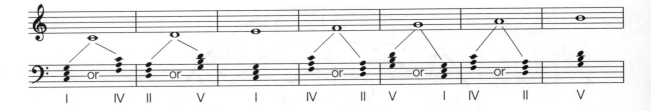

I   IV   II   V   I   IV   II   V   I IV   II   V

These points will help you to select your chords:

(1) It is not always suitable to give every melody note one chord. A long melody note may have two chords, like this:

     V   I

or one chord may be fitted to two or more melody notes:

    I   V

Generally, chords change less often than melody notes.

(2) Sometimes there are notes in a melody that do not belong to the chords underneath. For example, two melody notes that belong to the chords may be linked by a note which does not fit the harmony. The notes marked * here are examples:

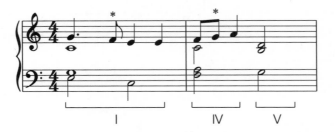

Such notes are called **passing notes**. There must not be a gap between a passing note and the harmony note on either side of it.

> **Remember!** A passing note is a note that makes a stepwise link between two harmony notes in a melodic line.

The simplest kind is a single passing note between tones that are a third apart, while harmony notes a second apart may be linked by a 'chromatic passing note'. Two or more passing notes can be used in succession. Passing notes are found in bass and middle parts as well as in melodies; they may be used simultaneously in different parts of the texture.

(3) Sometimes a harmony note in the melody is played twice, with the next note above or below it played in between. Again, the notes marked * are examples:

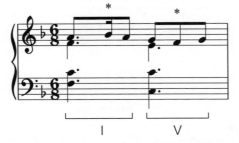

Notes of this kind are called **auxiliary notes**.

> **Remember!** An auxiliary note is a note that follows a harmony note by step, either above or below, but then returns to the *same* harmony note.

Exercise 1   **Choose suitable chords for the places marked** |1_____| |2_____| **etc. in the following melodies.**

Example

Traditional, 'Here we go round the mulberry bush'

Allegro

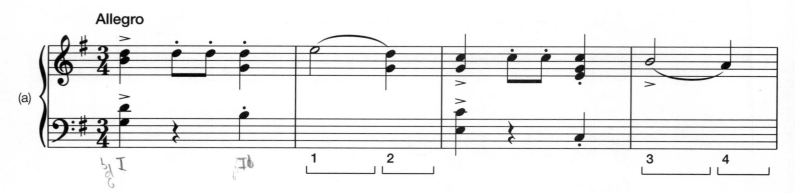

(a)

Allegretto

(b)

Traditional, 'Baa baa black sheep'

(c)

Con moto

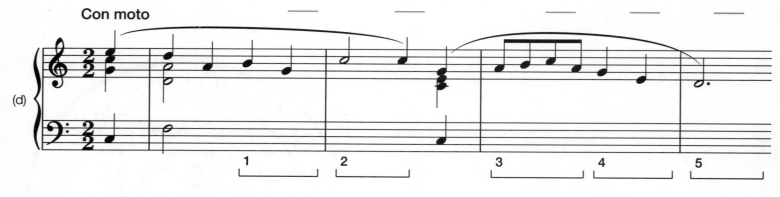

(d)

Traditional, 'Where are you going to, my pretty maid?'

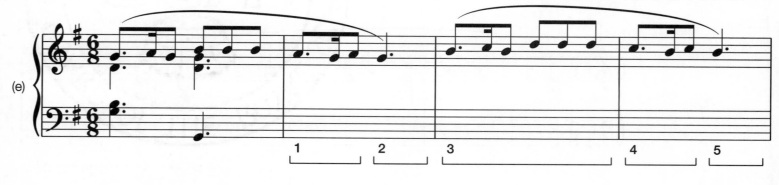

(e)

Performance directions

You will need to know the meaning of these Italian terms in Grade 5.

attacca	go straight on to the next section of music
dolente	sad, mournful
dolore	grief (*doloroso*: sorrowful)
doppio movimento	twice as fast
estinto	as soft as possible, lifeless
incalzando	getting quicker
lacrimoso	sad
loco	at the normal pitch (used to cancel an *8va* direction)
lunga	long (*lunga pausa*: long pause)
lusingando	coaxing, in a sweet and persuasive style
misura	measure (*alla misura*: in strict time; *senza misura*: in free time)
ossia	or, alternatively
piacevole	pleasant
piangevole	plaintive, in the style of a lament
pochettino, poch.	rather little
rinforzando, rf, rfz	reinforcing
segue	go straight on
smorzando, smorz.	dying away in tone and speed
teneramente, tenerezza	tenderly, tenderness
tosto	swift, rapid (but often used in the same sense as *troppo*)
volante	flying, fast

You will also need to know the meaning of these German terms.

aber	but
Ausdruck	expression
bewegt	with movement, agitated
breit	broad, expansive
ein	a, one
einfach	simple
etwas	somewhat, rather
fröhlich	cheerful, joyful
immer	always
langsam	slow
lebhaft	lively
mässig	at a moderate speed
mit	with
nicht	not
ohne	without
ruhig	peaceful
schnell	fast
sehr	very
süss	sweet
traurig	sad
und	and
voll	full
wenig	little
wieder	again
zart	tender, delicate
zu	to, too

You also need to understand the signs used to show reiterations and repeats (refer to *The AB Guide to Music Theory*, Chapter 13).

Instruments and voices

In Grade 5 you will need to know:
► the names of instruments,
► the clefs they use,
► instrument family groups, and
► the basic way by which they produce sound.

Page 43 in *Music Theory in Practice*, Grade 4, provides some basic facts; and *The AB Guide to Music Theory*, Part II, Chapters 19–21, give further information, although more than you will need to know at this stage.

You might also be asked questions on voices and the clefs they use. Page 23 of this book provides some basic facts and *The AB Guide to Music Theory*, Part II, Chapter 14, has more detailed information.

Exercise 1 ☑ The following passage is the opening of *Berceuse* by Russian composer, Ilynsky. Look through it, and then answer the questions below.

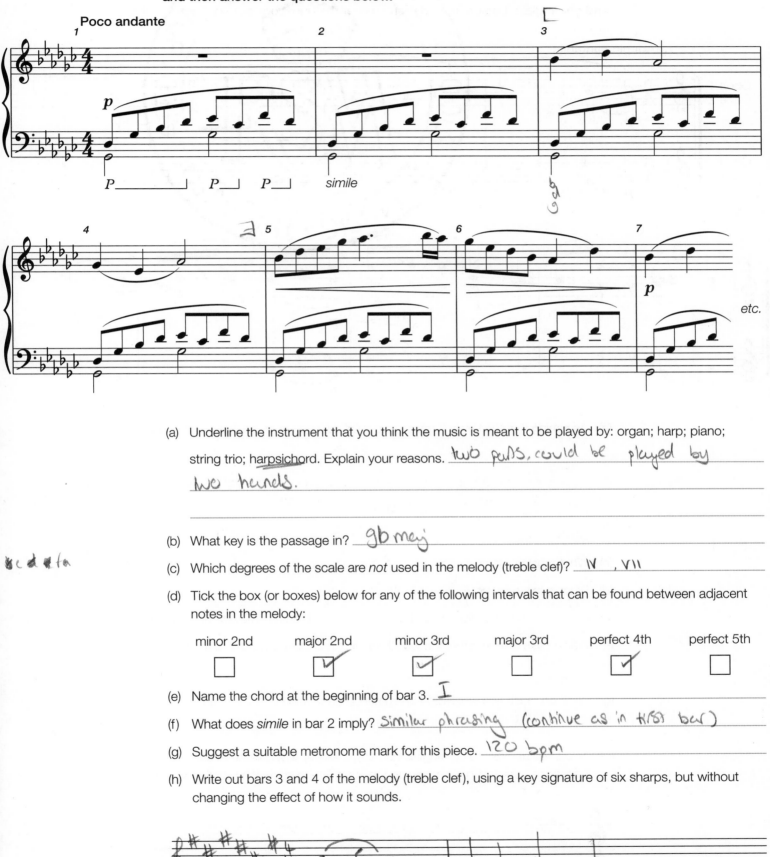

(a) Underline the instrument that you think the music is meant to be played by: organ; harp; piano; string trio; <u>harpsichord</u>. Explain your reasons. <u>two parts, could be played by two hands.</u>

(b) What key is the passage in? <u>Gb maj</u>

(c) Which degrees of the scale are *not* used in the melody (treble clef)? <u>IV , VII</u>

(d) Tick the box (or boxes) below for any of the following intervals that can be found between adjacent notes in the melody:

minor 2nd	major 2nd	minor 3rd	major 3rd	perfect 4th	perfect 5th
☐	☑	☑	☐	☑	☐

(e) Name the chord at the beginning of bar 3. <u>I</u>

(f) What does *simile* in bar 2 imply? <u>Similar phrasing (continue as in first bar)</u>

(g) Suggest a suitable metronome mark for this piece. <u>120 bpm</u>

(h) Write out bars 3 and 4 of the melody (treble clef), using a key signature of six sharps, but without changing the effect of how it sounds.

Exercise 2 ✔   The following passage is the opening of the second movement of Beethoven's Trio for 2 oboes and cor anglais. Look at it, and then answer the questions below.

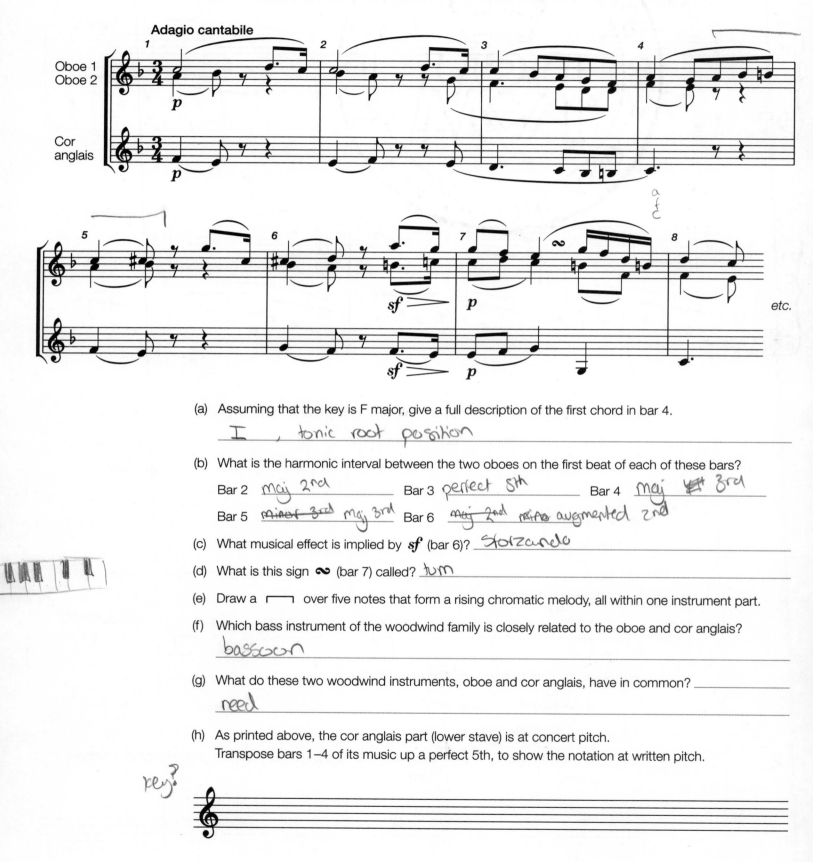

(a) Assuming that the key is F major, give a full description of the first chord in bar 4.

_____I_____, tonic root position_____

(b) What is the harmonic interval between the two oboes on the first beat of each of these bars?

Bar 2 _maj 2nd_ Bar 3 _perfect 5th_ Bar 4 _maj ♯ 3rd_

Bar 5 _minor 3rd maj 3rd_ Bar 6 _maj 2nd minor augmented 2nd_

(c) What musical effect is implied by **sf** (bar 6)? _sforzando_

(d) What is this sign ∽ (bar 7) called? _turn_

(e) Draw a ⌐‾‾⌐ over five notes that form a rising chromatic melody, all within one instrument part.

(f) Which bass instrument of the woodwind family is closely related to the oboe and cor anglais?

bassoon

(g) What do these two woodwind instruments, oboe and cor anglais, have in common? _____

reed

(h) As printed above, the cor anglais part (lower stave) is at concert pitch.
Transpose bars 1–4 of its music up a perfect 5th, to show the notation at written pitch.

key?

Exercise 3 ☑ The following passage is for 4-part choir. It comes at the end of a motet, *Ave verum*, by Mozart (the words are not shown). Look through it, and then answer the questions below.

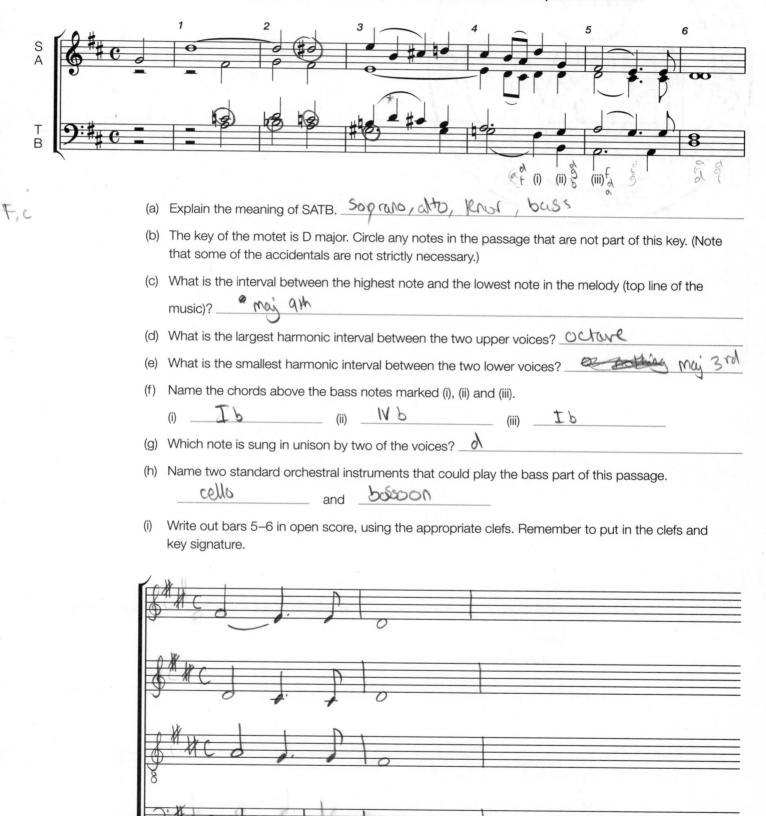

F, c

(a) Explain the meaning of SATB. *Soprano, alto, tenor, bass*

(b) The key of the motet is D major. Circle any notes in the passage that are not part of this key. (Note that some of the accidentals are not strictly necessary.)

(c) What is the interval between the highest note and the lowest note in the melody (top line of the music)? *maj 9th*

(d) What is the largest harmonic interval between the two upper voices? *octave*

(e) What is the smallest harmonic interval between the two lower voices? ~~nothing~~ *maj 3rd*

(f) Name the chords above the bass notes marked (i), (ii) and (iii).

(i) *Ib*   (ii) *IVb*   (iii) *Ib*

(g) Which note is sung in unison by two of the voices? *d*

(h) Name two standard orchestral instruments that could play the bass part of this passage.
cello and *bassoon*

(i) Write out bars 5–6 in open score, using the appropriate clefs. Remember to put in the clefs and key signature.

Exercise 4 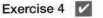 The following passage is from the last movement of Ravel's String Quartet, printed here on two staves (i.e. in short score). Look through it, and then answer the questions below.

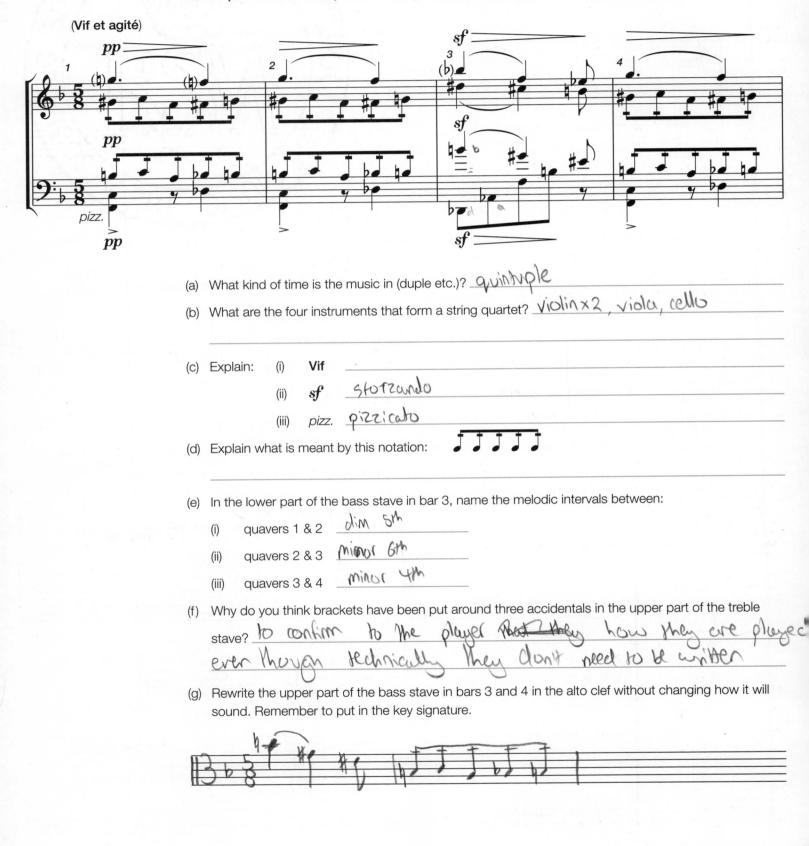

(a) What kind of time is the music in (duple etc.)? _quintuple_

(b) What are the four instruments that form a string quartet? _violin x2, viola, cello_

(c) Explain: (i) **Vif** _____

         (ii) *sf* _sforzando_

         (iii) *pizz.* _pizzicato_

(d) Explain what is meant by this notation: _____

(e) In the lower part of the bass stave in bar 3, name the melodic intervals between:

     (i) quavers 1 & 2 _dim 5th_

     (ii) quavers 2 & 3 _minor 6th_

     (iii) quavers 3 & 4 _minor 4th_

(f) Why do you think brackets have been put around three accidentals in the upper part of the treble stave? _to confirm to the player that they how they are played even though technically they don't need to be written_

(g) Rewrite the upper part of the bass stave in bars 3 and 4 in the alto clef without changing how it will sound. Remember to put in the key signature.